The Camel Spider or Wind Scorpion

The Complete Guide to Camel Spiders

All You Need to Know about Camel Spiders:
Facts Including Size, Speed, and Bite

by Hathai Ross

Copyright Page

Copyright Greenslopes Direct Publishing 2013

Foreword

I have been fascinated by spiders all of my life. The bigger they are, the more scary for me – none more so than the camel spider!

I have heard so many stories about these creatures that it is really difficult to know what the truth is. That is why this book has been written – to try and decipher fact from fiction.

Once you have read this book, you will know everything there is to know about these wonderfully strange creatures.

Acknowledgements

This book is dedicated to my lovely son Jacob, who always inspires me to write!

I would also like to thank all of my friends who have supported me while I have written this book. I could not have done it without you.

Also, without the help of my husband Duncan, this book would not be published.

Contents

The Complete Guide to Camel Spiders

The Complete Guide to Camel Spiders

The Complete Guide to Camel Spiders

Introduction to camel spiders

Camel spiders are sometimes referred to as wind scorpions or sun spiders. In recent years, interest in these mysterious creatures has grown significantly, and people have become very curious about them. This is encouraged by encounters between soldiers and camel spiders in the Middle East. Many stories and myths about camel spiders have emerged and it is now hard to tell what's true and what's not.

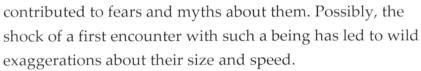

Camel spiders have a bloodcurdling appearance, which has undoubtedly contributed to fears and myths about them. Possibly, the shock of a first encounter with such a being has led to wild exaggerations about their size and speed.

The reputation of camel spiders is exemplified in the 2012 horror movie that shares the same name. The movie *Camel Spiders* is extremely gory; the spiders gruesomely attack American troops stationed in the desert. Camel spiders are portrayed as vicious, dangerous, and a serious threat to humanity. Of course, the movie is fictional, but it does show how legendary these creatures have become.

In addition, a novel entitled *The Camel Spider* has recently been published. This book is not actually about camel spiders, but does name a deadly member of a terrorist group after them.

Whether they are starring in horror films or being compared to terrorists, camel spiders definitely have a bad reputation. But are they really that dangerous? In this book, we will discover the facts about camel spiders: their appearance, size, and speed, what they eat, how they hunt, and whether they are poisonous. We will examine some common myths about camel spiders, as well as real encounters. This book also includes the story of a soldier who accidentally brought a camel spider home to the United Kingdom in his luggage!

What are camel spiders?

Are they spiders or scorpions?

Many people reasonably assume that camel spiders are indeed spiders. However, others refer to camel spiders as wind scorpions. This begs the question – are they spiders or scorpions?

In actual fact, camel spiders are not spiders or scorpions! Instead, the scientific name for a camel spider is a Solifugid.

Solifugae, spiders, and scorpions are all types of arachnids. Therefore, they do have very similar characteristics. For example, they all have eight legs. Similarities have often led to some confusion between the three.

The body of a camel spider looks very similar to that of an actual spider. It has two main parts: the cephalothorax and the opisthosoma. The former can basically be explained as the head merged with the thorax, whilst the latter is similar to an abdomen. Each section is made of several segments. When looking

The Complete Guide to Camel Spiders

at a camel spider, we can see that it does consist of these two sections, with the cephalothorax at the front.

Scorpions have an additional third section behind the abdomen: a tail that curves over the body with a sting at the end. Camel spiders do not have a tail.

Camel spiders have a fearsome jaw consisting of two pincers positioned at the front of the head, called *chelicerae*. This is what causes some people to compare and confuse them with scorpions or even crabs. This is different from spiders, which typically have fangs rather than pincers.

Camel spiders also differ from actual spiders because they do not spin webs.

So, despite being called both camel spiders and wind scorpions, Solifugae are actually unique.

Families and species

Solifugae are the sixth-most diverse form of arachnid. There are many species of camel spider – over a thousand, in fact. Each species can be assigned to one of 12 families.

An example of a camel spider family is the Mummuciidae family. There are approximately 18 known species in this family. They exist only in South America and are especially prevalent in Brazil.

Another example is the Galeodidae family, which includes 200 species of Solifugae. This family is distinguished from others because members have fine hairs on the lower, claw-like sections of their legs. This family of camel spider is prevalent in North Africa and across Asia.

The 10 other camel spider families are Ammotrechidae, Ceromidae, Daesiidae, Eremobatidae, Gylippidae, Hexisopodidae, Karschiidae, Melanoblossidae, Rhagodidae, and Solpugidae. These families each contain numerous sub-families and species.

Dividing camel spiders into different families and species allows scientists to classify and identify them easily. Each family has slight variations and different characteristics. For example, some families are curve-faced, whereas others are straight-faced. Families often exist in different regions, as well; we will look at this in more detail in chapter two.

We will not discuss all the species in detail in this book, but it is important to remember that they do exist and that there are differences between types of camel spiders.

Appearance and characteristics

We have already mentioned how a camel spider's body consists of two sections: the head and abdomen. The exact size and shape of these varies between species. Most camel spiders are a tan or light brown colour, not dissimilar to sand. This helps them to blend in with their environment and makes it harder for predators (for example, birds) to spot them.

However, not all camel spiders are tan-coloured. The Namibian Solifugae is dark brown, or black and white. These camel spiders are attempting to mimic Tenebrionid beetles. This is a form of aggressive mimicry, in which the camel spider is disguised as a relatively harmless and common beetle. The Namibian camel spider will then find it easier to approach and catch prey.

Tenebrionid Beetle

Camel Spider

The Complete Guide to Camel Spiders

Most camel spiders are quite hairy; this is to aid their sensory perception.

Camel spiders also appear to have 10 legs. In actual fact, the first pair of 'legs' are pedipalps. These pedipalps are another appendage that helps sensory perception. Unlike the other four pairs of legs, the pedipalps do not touch the floor. Instead, they are held out in front of the camel spider as it moves. This enables the camel spider to sense layout of the environment and feel obstacles and prey. The other eight legs are used for running and movement. The two pairs directly behind the pedipalps are thinner and smaller than the back pairs. This is because most of the energy comes from the posterior legs, with the other pairs aiding balance and agility. The legs have seven segments,

whereas the pedipalps only have five.

At the tip of their pedipalps, camel spiders have small adhesive organs. This sticky part can be used to catch flying prey and to help climb sheer or smooth surfaces.

Camel spiders' pincers (chelicerae) are very prominent and can be up to one-third of their entire body

15

length, meaning that, relative to their size, they have the largest jaws in the whole world. This is quite an impressive fact and does help to explain why people feel shocked and threatened at first sight. A camel spider's chelicerae also have teeth positioned along the pincers; these teeth help to rip through the skin of prey and gnaw through flesh. The number of teeth depends on the species of camel spider in question.

Camel spiders sometimes rub their pincers together and, in doing so, create a sort of rattling sound. This is known as stridulation, the rubbing together of body parts to create a sound. The purpose is sometimes to attract a mate, or it can be threatening: a warning sign that the camel spider is preparing to attack or defend itself. Again, this can be quite alarming for people when they first see camel spiders, particularly if they do not know what the sound is or what it signifies.

Camel spiders' eyes are positioned centrally on their heads, above the jaw. They vary in size; in some species, they can grow to be quite large, but in others, they remain fairly small. Surprisingly, their eyesight is quite sophisticated.

Camel spiders can see shapes and forms, and do use their vision to find prey and avoid predators.

Camel spiders have developed several capacities for retaining fluids. This is not dissimilar to cacti, which can tolerate extreme dryness; they have been known to survive for years in the desert without even a drop of rain. The main challenge facing camel spiders is remaining at an appropriate body temperature without  losing all their fluids very fast. Camel spiders gain water from the body fluids of their prey. They have an extremely low rate of respiration and can conserve water for a long time.

Camel spiders are also largely nocturnal or crepuscular (active at dawn and dusk). This is because, in some areas that camel spiders inhabit, it is too hot during the day to spend time in the sunlight. The scientific name for camel spider is Solifugae, which in Latin means "those who flee from the sun" (Live Science 2013). Camel spiders prefer to avoid the hottest part of the day and instead venture out when it is cooler. Again, this measure allows camel spiders to conserve fluids. During the hot hours, they remain in burrows (we will look at this in more detail in chapter two). A few species of camel spider can withstand the heat and do go out to hunt during the middle of the day. Presumably, this is why some people refer to camel spiders as sun spiders.

It is safe to say that camel spiders are not the best looking creatures on earth. However, when we consider the ways in which they have evolved to be able to live in harsh environments, camel spiders are actually very impressive. They have developed numerous attributes and characteristics in order to survive. Although it is not particularly attractive, the body of a camel spider does have a purpose that it manages to fulfil very successfully.

Size

The size of camel spiders is often drastically exaggerated. This can be attributed to the shock of a first meeting or simply the threatening appearance, which can make the creature seem larger than it really is.

Reports have compared the size of a camel spider to hubcaps, plates, and Frisbees. However, in actual fact, it is impossible (or at least highly unlikely) for a camel spider to grow to this size.

Size does vary between families and species. Some species of camel spider are relatively small Arachnids, only reaching a few millimetres or centimetres. The larger species can grow to be 12 to 15 centimetres, or five to six inches, including the legs. The body of such a spider would be about seven centimetres. Whilst this would be quite alarming on first sight, it cannot reasonably be compared to a hubcap. However, we cannot rule out the possibility that larger camel spiders may be out there.

19

The Complete Guide to Camel Spiders

In terms of weight, camel spiders can grow to be two ounces, or 56 grams. This is about the same as two slices of bread.

It is worth noting that male camel spiders are usually smaller than their female counterparts. However, they also normally have longer legs than females.

Speed

The speed of camel spiders is also exaggerated. People have claimed that they have seen camel spiders running at 50 kilometres per hour. This would mean that camel spiders could move as fast as house cats. Scientific studies and recordings show that this is not possible.

In reality, camel spiders have a top speed of 16 kilometres per hour (approximately 10 miles per hour). This is not as fast as some people might claim, but it is still faster than many other invertebrates. Camel spiders have adapted to run fast and efficiently over land in order to hunt. For example, they have an open respiratory system and breathe via a trachea. This means that oxygen can be taken on and distributed to tissue very fast. Because of this, camel spiders can run quickly.

Camel spiders are renowned for their sprinting ability. However, they are not so good at long distance running. They tend to run in short bursts, rather than over extended periods of time.

Depending on their species and country of origin, camel spiders cover varying terrain, some of which is quite challenging, such as sand, stones, and forests. Some species of camel spider are excellent climbers. In addition to this, individual camel spiders can cover significant areas when searching for food and hunting. To aid this lifestyle, they have developed to be agile and efficient movers.

Mating

The mating of camel spiders has not been widely observed. In fact, only a few species have been seen and recorded mating. However, we can assume that the mating behaviour of these observed species is the general pattern of behaviour for most camel spiders.

First, a camel spider might stridulate to try and attract a mate. In other species, males simply wander around looking for a mate, in the same way that they look for food. Some males can mate numerous times in a short period of time.

Most female camel spiders must eat substantial amounts of food in the period leading up to mating. This is because she will not leave the burrow where she will lay her eggs until they hatch. Therefore, it is vital for the female to have enough body fat prior to mating to survive this period.

Once a viable mate has been found, the male camel spider either simply grabs the female, or he starts to stroke her and rub her with his pedipalps, causing her to fall into a sleepy, passive state.

The male then pushes the abdomen of the female upwards. This reveals the female's genital orifice. The male camel spider then inserts his pincer in order to open the orifice.

Next, the male produces a sperm-like substance. In some species, the male transfers this substance directly into the female's genitals. In others, the male picks up the sperm-like substance with his pincer, and inserts it into the female this way.

The male camel spider then rubs or chews the female's abdomen; this has been compared to a massage. The female starts to wake up from her stupor. At this point, the mating session is complete, and the male spider moves away. The whole process takes only a few minutes.

The females sometimes consume male camel spiders after mating. It is estimated that this happens around 40 per cent of the time. People have suggested that this is why males 'massage' the female after inserting their sperm – to try to appease her and avoid being eaten. Other males simply move away and escape before the female has a chance to regain full consciousness and come out of her stupor.

It is generally thought that even if they are not eaten by the female, male camel spiders die a fairly short time after mating. However, we must remember that not many species of camel spider have been scientifically observed whilst mating. Therefore, we cannot be certain that the same patterns apply to all species of camel spider.

Breeding

Once mating has taken place, the female camel spider then finds a safe and protected place to lay her eggs. Most of the time, this involves the female digging a burrow in the ground. The female lays her eggs several days or weeks later.

Female camel spiders can produce up to 200 eggs at a time, although some species produce a lot fewer. It has been recognised that, after mating once, some types of camel spider can produce more than one batch of eggs, whereas others cannot.

As we have already mentioned, the female can stay with the eggs, guarding them, until they hatch. However, this is not true for all species of camel spider. This period varies significantly between species and depending on environment (for example, temperature and humidity). It can be anywhere between two days and two months! Again, this is why female camel spiders have to eat so much before mating.

Like male camel spiders, the females often die shortly after their breeding responsibilities are complete.

All but one species has been observed to be univoltine, meaning that they only have one brood of young per year. The one exception is a camel spider from the Namib Desert in Southern Africa, which has been recorded as bivoltine, producing two broods of young per year. Most camel spiders don't survive longer than one year (we will look at this in more detail in the lifespan section of this chapter). Taking these two pieces of information together, it is logical to assume that most female camel spiders only produce one brood during their lifetimes. However, this is by no means set in stone as some camel spiders do live longer. Relatively little research has been done into such areas.

'Post-embryos' or 'larvae' are common terms for freshly-hatched eggs. From documented observations, we can say that the appearance of post-embryos varies considerably between species. However, post-embryos are generally pretty much immobile for the first few days, because their legs are not properly developed. This immobility continues until the first 'moult' (shedding of the exoskeleton), which normally happens several days after the eggs hatch.

At this stage, the young camel spiders are sociable, and choose to remain living in the burrow with their siblings, in loosely organised communities. They go through several nymphal instars (developmental stages) before they reach maturity. Each stage involves shedding the exoskeleton and undergoing changes in body proportions, colour, and shape. The camel spiders grow new segments and undergo other developments. Many insects go through similar instars. Young camel spiders usually go through four or five of these stages. However, some species can go through up to nine nymphal instars before they reach maturity.

Once these early stages of development are complete, it is time for the young camel spider to venture out of the burrow and begin life alone.

Lifespan

The average lifespan of a camel spider is less than one year in the wild, although camel spiders have been known to live for up to three years.

The lifespan for camel spiders depends on their species, and also the environment in which they are living. For example, the amount of prey and potential food in an area, and the number of predators the camel spider has, all affect the lifespan of particular camel spiders. It is generally thought that most species of camel spider die shortly after breeding.

History of the camel spider

A heightened interest in camel spiders has developed only recently. This is mainly due to war in the Middle East, particularly in Iraq, and the subsequent stories soldiers have relayed back to the West about these creatures.

This explains why we do not know a lot about the history of camel spiders; much of their natural history remains unknown. However, some research has been done in this area, which we will now look at.

Camel spiders are undoubtedly a monophyletic group: all camel spiders are descendent from one single ancestor, one stock. This has been discovered through molecular and morphological analysis, meaning that scientists have focused on both the genetics and the structural form of camel spiders.

In terms of fossil history, the available evidence is very limited. Only a handful of useful camel spider fossils have been found. A 300 million year old fossil discovered in Poland does show some features that link it to camel spiders, such as large pincers. However, we cannot be certain that this is a fossil of an early camel spider; it is simply classed as an Arachnid.

The oldest fossil that can, without doubt, be classed as a camel spider dates back 305 million years. It was found in Illinois, USA. Even though it is clearly a camel spider, this fossil is not well-preserved or complete.

A camel spider fossil dating back 115 million years can tell us useful information about the Ceromidae family. It shows that this family of camel spider lived on an ancient continent, which has now broken up. The continent split and is now South America and South Africa. We can see that the Ceromidae spiders on the South African part have survived to the present day, whereas South American Ceromidae spiders have not. This is very interesting bio-geographical information, which has prompted further research. This fossil has also given us further clues about the appearance of camel spiders throughout history.

An extremely well-preserved fossil was found in Baltic amber; it is thought to be between 40 and 50 million years old. The fossil shows a small  male camel spider, only about five millimetres in length. However, it tells us that camel spiders used to inhabit Northern Europe. This is obviously well beyond their current range and is a surprising find.

The most recent camel spider fossil comes from the Dominican Republic and is around 10 to 30 million years old. It has been assigned to the Ammotrechidae family and fits with modern-day examples of this family from America and the Caribbean Islands.

If we look at a more recent history of camel spiders, we can note that the Ancient Greeks recognised the difference between camel spiders and actual spiders; they assigned different names to the two.

We can also see references to camel spiders from both World War 1 and World War 2. Soldiers would refer to them as 'jerrymanders' and would stage fights and place bets on them. For example, in World War I, troops stationed in Egypt used to bet on fights between individual camel spiders. During World War II, the stakes grew higher as camel spiders were pitted against scorpions in Libya.

The history of camel spiders is fascinating, even though relatively little is known about these mysterious creatures. We hope that further discoveries will be made so that we can learn more about camel spiders in the future.

Where do camel spiders live?

Countries

Camel spiders are typically associated with countries in the Middle East, such as Iraq and Afghanistan, because of reports from Western soldiers. However, they actually inhabit many hot countries, including countries in Africa and the Americas. Different families and species can be found in varying countries or continents. Therefore, the question 'Where do camel spiders live?' is actually a lot

more complicated than it first appears. The answer is not simply 'in Iraq,' or 'in the desert.'

Camel spiders from the Ammotrechidae and Eremobatidae families can be found in Northern and Central America, for example, in Arizona and Texas in the US, and in Mexico. Ammotrechidae camel spiders can also be found in South America and the Caribbean Islands. The Mummuciidae family lives in South America, in countries like Brazil, Peru, and Bolivia.

The Complete Guide to Camel Spiders

Camel spiders are quite prevalent in Africa. Ceromidae and Hexisopodidae families are found only in Southern Africa. This includes, but is not limited to, countries like Namibia, Botswana, and South Africa. The Melanoblossidae family provides a particularly interesting case, as they are known in several Southern African countries but also in the Southeast Asian countries of Vietnam and Indonesia. They are the only camel spiders to be found this far east. This raises fascinating research questions about how they came to inhabit these two very different and distant areas.

Members of the Gylippidae family are found in Southern Africa and across Central Asia.

Other families of camel spider – Solpugidae, Galeodidae, Rhagodidae, Karschiidae, and Daesiidae – are found in Northern Africa and across the Middle East and Central Asia. Some camel spiders are even found further south, in India. It is highly likely that the many stories told by Western soldiers are about one of these families of camel spider.

In addition to Africa and Asia, members of the Daesiidae family are also found in South America and Southern Europe; this is probably the most widespread camel spider family.

If we were to look at the various species within families, we could go into more detail. However, this is a basic overview of places where you might find a camel spider.

One point of interest is that no camel spiders have been found in Australia. Lots of unusual species of true spiders are found there, and camel spiders have made it as far as Vietnam and even Indonesia, so why not Australia? Scientists remain puzzled by this, because the hot and dry conditions in Australia seem perfect for a camel spider. This just goes to show that there are still lots of unknowns about camel spiders.

The Complete Guide to Camel Spiders

Environment

Camel spiders are often associated with desert environments: places that receive less than 250 millimetres of rain a year. Most species of camel spider inhabit areas like this, possibly causing camel spiders to be referred to as

'sun spiders.' For example, species within the Solpugidae, Galeodidae, Rhagodidae, and Karschiidae families are normally found in places with substantial desert regions, as are others.

Living in the desert means there is little vegetation and low humidity; the environment often includes sands dunes and rocky areas.

These camel spiders must be able to cope with very high temperatures during the day and often quite low temperatures at night. They must also be able to survive without much water (we have already discussed how camel spiders are adapted to this in the 'appearance and characteristics' section in Chapter 1).

Despite being typically associated with the desert, some families and species of camel spider live elsewhere.

For example, some camel spiders inhabit dry grasslands. However, the places are still very hot and have low humidity.

An unusual case is the Melanoblossidae family; as we have previously mentioned, these spiders can be found in Vietnam and Indonesia. This is surprising as these places are generally thought of as quite humid and rainy – very different from the desert environments normally associated with camel spiders.

No matter where camel spiders live, they do have similar habits when it comes to burrowing, or nesting. Because they typically live  in very hot environments, it is vital for camel spiders to have a place to take shelter and avoid the hottest part of the day.

Depending on where they live and the resources available to them, this can involve simply hiding under a rock or in a shaded crevice, or it can mean constructing a burrow.

Camel spiders are likely to spend a lot of time in their burrows or in shaded places. It is where they will retreat when they are not hunting or searching for a mate. Female camel spiders will lay their eggs, and the young will spend their first few days in the safety of a burrow. It offers protection from both the sun and predators.

What do camel spiders eat?

Food

Camel spiders are carnivorous; this means that their preferred method of getting food is to hunt and kill other creatures or to scavenge for them. When people mention carnivores, we often think of lions, tigers, and other large predators. However, creatures that eat insects are also classed as carnivores. Camel spiders actually eat a wide range of prey, and they also eat a substantial amount of it, due to an unusually high metabolism.

It is important to remember that many anecdotes and stories are told about the eating habits of camel spiders; these can be untrue or exaggerated. For example, some people have claimed that camel spiders eat the stomachs of camels. In actual fact, camel spiders mostly eat insects, spiders, lizards, small snakes, and rodents. They have also been known to eat small birds.

Next, we will look at how camel spiders catch prey and the bizarre way in which they consume it.

The Complete Guide to Camel Spiders

Hunting

The hunting behaviour of camel spiders has not been widely observed. However, it appears that most species travel around searching for food. They often run in short bursts and can cover quite large areas of ground.

Most camel spiders seem to move randomly when hunting, without a particular direction or destination. However, in some species, the act of stalking prey has been observed, though this is thought to be quite rare. Members of the Hexisopodidae family, inhabiting Southern Africa, are not normally seen above ground. Instead, they often hunt and forage beneath the surface, buried a short distance below the sand.

Previously, scientists believed that camel spiders relied almost entirely on their tactile senses when locating prey, simply using their pedipalps to feel around for potential creatures to consume. Recent studies have confirmed this. However, they have also alleged that, in addition, camel spiders do use their vision when hunting.

It has been suggested that camel spiders can feel vibrations through the ground around them, be it soil or sand, using the sensory organs on their legs. These sensory organs are called malleoli or rachet/racket organs. The true function of these malleoli was, for a long time, unknown.

However, now scientists believe one main function is to aid in prey detection.

Camel spiders have a reputation for being fearsome hunters, and this is undoubtedly how they obtain the vast majority of their food. However, there is some evidence that camel spiders can, on occasion, become scavengers. They have been observed consuming creatures that have already been killed. For example, camel spiders have been seen eating snakes and lizards that have been hit by vehicles and ended up as road kill.

The evidence strongly suggests that camel spiders are opportunistic hunters, simply wandering around looking for any sort of potential prey. They are required to eat a lot; as previously mentioned, they have an unusually high metabolism for their size. Therefore, if they come across something edible that is already dead, they take the opportunity for a free meal.

Feeding behaviour

What do camel spiders do once they have located potential prey?

The first contact with prey is often made with the pedipalps, the first set of leg-like appendages. These pedipalps feel around, locating and positioning prey. The adhesive organs at the tips of the pedipalps are particularly useful for catching prey and holding it in place. These adhesive organs appear to use a kind of suction technique to grip prey.

Some species of camel spider conduct 'preparation' once they have captured their prey. This involves sawing off certain body parts from the prey using their chelicerae (pincers). For example, the head, wings, and antennae are often removed. This sounds very bizarre, but it is because these body parts contain higher levels of chitin. Chitin is similar to glucose, and, in terms of its function, to protein. Therefore, preparing prey allows the camel spider to efficiently consume the nutrients it requires. It is important to remember that such processes have only been observed in a few species of camel spider.

Once the camel spider is ready to eat, it holds the prey in position with the pedipalps and stabs at the prey with its pincers, piercing the skin. Next, the camel spider begins to macerate prey; the body starts to break down because it is made wet with digestive juices produced by the camel spider. The camel spider uses its teeth-lined pincers to gnaw and rub the exoskeleton of prey, grinding it down and extracting liquid. This extraction of liquid is how camel spiders take on water in the desert; this is vital to survival.

The feeding techniques of camel spiders are fascinating because they do not use venom. They simply break down their prey and suck out the body fluids. Hopefully, in the future, more research will be done into exactly how this process works.

A camel spider's predators

Despite being fearsome predators themselves, camel spiders can be on the receiving end. Several types of animals and reptiles are known to eat camel spiders. However, scientists are still unsure as to whether these creatures specifically target camel spiders, possibly because they are highly nutritious, or whether the camel spiders in question are simply unlucky and in the wrong place at the wrong time.

Various species of birds have been proven to prey upon camel spiders: most commonly raptors and owls, but also larks, bustards, and wagtails. Scientists have discovered the remains of camel spiders in the droppings of these birds.

In Botswana, bat-eared foxes regularly hunt camel spiders. Other small mammals (such as silver foxes, African civets, and jackals) have also been recorded consuming camel

The Complete Guide to Camel Spiders

spiders. This list is not exclusive, as at least 14 species of small mammals have been observed eating camel spiders.

Reptiles are also hunters of camel spiders – in particular, a species of gecko located in the Chihuahuan Desert, which stretches over the border between the United States and Mexico. Camel spiders are the fourth-most prevalent food type in the diet of these geckos. This does suggest that something about camel spiders makes them particularly appealing to the geckos. However, we cannot be sure about this. Several reptiles in Southern Africa are also associated with eating camel spiders, but such reports are not supported by scientific research.

Even other Arachnids, such as spiders, can eat camel spiders, and they have also been known to eat each other. We can see that, although they have a reputation for being voracious predators, camel spiders are not without vulnerabilities and can become the prey.

How dangerous are camel spiders?

Are they poisonous?

'Are camel spiders poisonous?' is a commonly-asked question.

Many people assume that camel spiders can secrete poison. Often, people are terrified that if a camel spider bites them, they will be dead within minutes. This assumption probably stems partly from the size of their pincers, and also the fact that many other spiders do administer venom via their fangs.

However, camel spiders are not venomous. As we have mentioned, they can use digestive juices in order to help break down the bodies of their prey, but they do not possess poison. The fact that they are not poisonous does not mean they are not dangerous predators; they can still do significant damage with their oversized pincers.

Do they bite?

Camel spiders do not have venom, but they do have a powerful jaw that can inflict a serious bite.

For prey, the bite of a camel spider is nearly always deadly. Thanks to the sticky section of their pedipalps, it is very hard to escape from the jaws of a camel spider. The stabbing and grinding process crushes the bodies of victims and breaks them down quickly. As previously mentioned, camel spiders' pincers are extremely large in comparison with the rest of their bodies; they make up one third of the whole body. Therefore, their bite is extremely powerful for their size. To many creatures, the bite of a camel spider is fatal.

Fortunately, the bite is not fatal to humans. However, it is certainly something to be avoided if at all possible, as it can do some nasty damage.

Camel spiders do not often bite humans, unless they are provoked. Rumours about camel spiders chasing humans have circulated, but these are untrue; they prefer to run away from creatures that are significantly larger than them. However, some unlucky people do get bitten. This is normally in situations where a camel spider has taken refuge in a tent or house, and the person has unwittingly rolled over on to the camel spider or touched it in some way by accident.

The Complete Guide to Camel Spiders

Although it is not poisonous, the bite of a camel spider can become infected very quickly due to the saliva secreted (normally, this is to help break down prey) and the remnants of the rotting flesh of recent victims. An infection can result in severe pain. Therefore, it is important to make sure you receive the correct first aid and treatment if you are bitten by a camel spider. Cleaning and bandaging the area is important.

Can you touch a camel spider?

People are often extremely scared to touch camel spiders, assuming that they are poisonous and deadly. However, they are not as dangerous as they look.

If you can catch a camel spider before it runs away, it is possible to touch it, although it is important to be cautious. There are many pictures of people holding camel spiders, often by the legs – so as to avoid the pincer area. If you do try to touch a camel spider, do so at your own risk! It is likely that the creature will try to bite, because it will feel trapped and threatened.

Can you eat camel spiders?

The simple answer to this question is, yes, you can eat camel spiders.

Bear Grylls eats a camel spider in an episode of the 2006 series *Man vs. Wild*. He starts by removing the pincers and pedipalps, before popping the rest of the camel spider's body into his mouth, describing it as "a good bit of protein and energy" (http://www.youtube.com/watch?v=cJRpXYs1pQA). It is hard not to cringe as Grylls bites into the camel spider; he states that it is like an explosion of pus in his mouth.

Grylls also documents the consumption of a camel spider in his book *Mission Survival 3: Sands of the Scorpion*. The sensation is described in a very unpleasant way: "The innards were gooey and oozed between my teeth, as if I had just swallowed a gobbet of snot" (Grylls 2009 pp. 96).

So, it is possible to eat a camel spider. However, it is guaranteed to be a horrible experience. Most would advise against it, unless you are starving in the desert and in desperate need of nutrients, or unless someone will be paying you a vast amount in the form of a bet.

Reports of camel spider bites

Lance Corporal Sammy O'Gorman

The case of Lance Corporal Sammy O'Gorman is a good example of how an infection from a camel spider bite can be extremely dangerous if left untreated.

When flying to Iraq, spiders were probably the last thing on O'Gorman's mind. Roadside bombs and Improvised Explosive Devices (IEDs) are, after all, the main dangers for soldiers in Iraq. If someone steps on an IED, they are likely to lose a foot or a leg, and in some cases they are killed.

However, this is not what happened to O'Gorman. Instead, he was bitten by a camel spider. He did not notice the spider on him or even feel the bite initially; the only evidence was two small holes in his thigh. As the day went on, O'Gorman's bite became inflamed, but the onsite medic could not help him, and it was two weeks before he saw a doctor. The doctor drained some fluid from O'Gorman's leg, but the real problem was left unsolved.

O'Gorman went home on leave. Although he did not fully understand what the problem was, O'Gorman knew the infection was still there and getting worse). He  returned to his base in Germany, but shortly after, he was admitted to hospital. O'Gorman was taken immediately into intensive care, where it was established that his blood was infected. Without treatment, he had hours to live. Doctors feared that O'Gorman would not survive. However, 17 operations later, and with a significant portion of flesh from his thigh missing, O'Gorman was on the mend.

O'Gorman was bitten by the camel spider in 2009; it has taken three years for him to recover, and he was lucky to keep his leg. This account shows us how vital it is to treat camel spider bites with extreme caution. Even though they are not venomous, it is crucial to treat any infection early on to avoid the situation getting serious, as in O'Gorman's case.

UFC fighter Stephan Bonnar

Stephan Bonnar is well-known in the Ultimate Fighting Championship (UFC) circuit, and he has a reputation for wearing outrageous t-shirts. However, it came as a surprise when his choice of clothing caused him to have a run-in with a camel spider.

Bonnar went to Bahrain to visit the American troops stationed there. By all accounts the trip was a success, until his unfortunate choice of shirt (depicting a man in a turban getting his head blown off) caused Bonnar to be detained when trying to catch his return flight. Bonnar missed the flight and had to stay at the airport in Bahrain.

It was during this impromptu night at the airport that Bonnar was bitten by a camel spider.

Bonnar felt a burning sensation in his lower leg; he reached down to investigate what was going on, and found himself confronted with a camel spider. Despite Bonnar's attempts to catch and get a good look at it, the camel spider quickly ran off.

Overnight, Bonnar's leg swelled up, and he developed a fever. At first, he was not too worried because he was due to fly out the next day, thanks to some speedy re-scheduling. However, that flight was cancelled. Bonnar knew that the bite was getting infected, but he did not want to admit himself into hospital in Bahrain and further extend his stay. He decided to take three different types of antibiotic instead and stick it out for another night. Fortunately, he was able to fly home the following day.

It is unlikely that doctors would recommend taking three different types of antibiotics at once to treat a camel spider bite. They would much prefer it if victims simply went to hospital or to a doctor. However, Bonnar's story again shows us how fast an infection can cause noticeable symptoms and the importance of treating the bite quickly.

Do people keep camel spiders as pets?

Advice on keeping camel spiders as pets

It is possible to keep camel spiders as pets. However, important considerations need to be made before you get a pet camel spider.

Firstly, having some experience in keeping exotic pets is valuable – specifically, experience caring for exotic spiders, like tarantulas or scorpions. Experience is recommended because there are lots of considerations when keeping exotic pets that differ from keeping normal ones. Although in captivity camel spiders only live between one year and one and a half years, it is still important to think carefully before getting one as a pet, because they require a high level of care and expertise. They also have a painful (although not poisonous) bite, which you are at greater risk of if you choose to keep a camel spider in your home.

If you do decide to get a pet camel spider, there are several vital purchases you need to make before you bring the camel spider home.

First, an escape-proof enclosure is needed, unless you want to run the risk of waking up next to your camel spider. Remember, camel spiders can climb up glass and bite through wire with their pincers. Ideally, the enclosure

55

will consist of a large plastic tank with a lid and air holes, not an open top.

Camel spiders normally dig burrows or shelter under rocks in their natural habitats. Therefore, to make the tank as camel spider-friendly as possible, put a thick layer of sand at the bottom; about 10 to 13 centimetres is appropriate. This will allow camel spiders to shelter their whole bodies beneath the sand. It is also good to add branches, tree bark, or rocks to the tank. This will help to re-create the natural environment for camel spiders and provide extra shelter.

The next consideration if you want to keep camel spiders as pets is the temperature that they require. Camel spiders normally live in very hot climates, so it is necessary to re-create this if you want to keep one at home. A camel spider's living space should be kept at 35 degrees Celsius during the day. It should also be kept dry and not at all humid. Every evening, a slight mist of moisture should be added to the tank, to resemble the nighttime humidity in the desert. The temperature should then drop to somewhere between 24 and 28 degrees Celsius. This is quite complicated and challenging to re-create; temperature is probably one of the more difficult things about keeping a camel spider as a pet.

Once you bring the camel spider home, feeding becomes the main job. Camel spiders eat a surprisingly large amount given their size. If you are keeping a camel spider in captivity, you should aim to feed it prey the same size as your camel spider's abdomen every other day. You should feed them a range of insects, such as mealworms,  crickets, cockroaches, and locusts. You can also buy some 'frozen mice fluffs,' frozen baby mice for feeding exotic pets, and offer these about once a week. It is also advisable to place a small dish of water in the tank. In the wild, camel spiders get their water by sucking the body fluids out of prey. However, the replication of this is not guaranteed in captivity, because the prey is not fresh. Therefore, having a dish of water in the tank allows camel spiders to replenish their water supply if needed.

Do not put any other pets in the tank with the camel spider; they are not sociable animals and will more than likely try to consume any tank mates.

When it comes to handling your pet camel spider, there is some very simple advice – don't. Camel spiders will bite humans if they feel threatened, which is likely if they are picked up. Bites, although not poisonous, are painful and can become infected easily. No amount of handling will tame camel spiders. If you are hoping that your pet will 'get used' to being picked up, you are wrong; camel

57

spiders are wild animals. Wearing thick gloves is advisable when feeding your camel spider. Feeding should be done as quickly as possible, and the lid should be replaced on the cage immediately after feeding is complete.

These are just some of the considerations you should make if you are thinking about getting a camel spider as a pet. Could you look after the creature properly and re-create its natural habitat? Are you sure that a camel spider is what you are looking for in a pet? Remember camel spiders are not cuddly pets, and handling should be avoided. Because of this, camel spiders are not appropriate pets for everyone.

Stories of pet camel spiders

There are several examples on YouTube of people who keep camel spiders as pets.

TarantulaAddict has uploaded a video depicting a camel spider in captivity feeding on a locust (http://www.youtube. com /watch?v=Kq_JMgDDIiw). The video is very close-up and shows how interesting it can be to keep camel spiders as pets; watching their feeding behaviour closely gives a fascinating insight into their lives. The same owner, TarantulaAddict, has uploaded a second video entitled Angry camel spider, which shows the stridulating action, when camel spiders rub their pincers together to make a noise (http://www.youtube.com/watch?v =ommiDuKb8iE). Camel spiders do this when they feel threatened. Again, this video shows what can be observed if you have a camel spider as a pet and how interesting this can be.

Another YouTuber, Dan Oakley, has uploaded several videos of his pet camel spider 'Hades.' The first of these, entitled 'Hades my SUPER FRIENDLY CAMEL SPIDER' (http://www.youtube.com /watch?v=BejAWXq15mA), shows the owner (we can assume this is Dan Oakley) move a rock in the bottom of a tank to reveal Hades hiding underneath. Oakley then attempts to pick up the camel spider with bare hands. Oakley does manage this, although some might argue that 'super friendly' is a significant

59

exaggeration. (Readers should remember that handling camel spiders is not advised.) The second half of the video is Oakley talking about the camel spider and showing close-up the legs and pedipalps. This, combined with the visual close-up, does provide useful information about camel spiders and makes them appear slightly more appealing as a pet. In the comments below the video, Oakley mentions that this camel spider only lived for three weeks.

We can conclude that camel spiders may be interesting to keep as pets, but the experience is more observational than interactive. If you are hoping for a loveable pet that you can grow attached too, you should probably look elsewhere. However, these stories of people with camel spiders as pets do show that, for the right owner, keeping a camel spider can be very exciting and rewarding.

Fighting camel spiders

Camel spiders fighting each other

World War I was the start of a trend among soldiers, involving capturing camel spiders and setting up fights between them. Bets would often be made on these fights. This was a form of entertainment and a way of passing the time while stationed in Egypt during the war.

People's fascination with fighting camel spiders lives on, particularly as camel spiders are now well-known and have a fearsome reputation.

There is a video on YouTube of two camel spiders locked in a brutal fight (http://www.youtube.comwatch?v=RMP3F1Vs Ckg). This video was shot in Northern Iraq in 2007, showing that interest in camel spider battles is still alive and well in war-afflicted areas. In this video, the two spiders appear quite evenly matched at the start; their pincers are locked together in what is clearly going to be a vicious duel to the death. One spider has a larger abdomen than the other, suggesting that it is possibly a female or that it has recently fed.

As the video goes on, we can see that the smaller spider is actually beginning to dominate the fight. The pincers of the larger camel spider have been forced apart

61

leaving the head area vulnerable to the stabs and bites of the smaller camel spider. Needless to say, the video is quite gruesome.

Writhing and close to death, the larger camel spider is then flipped over onto its back as the smaller one delivers the final stabs to the head. This is extremely graphic, and you can almost sense the moment the larger camel spider dies, although it does continue twitching for some time.

The parting shot is of the smaller camel spider starting to consume its victim by gnawing on one of the legs.

We can see that these camel spiders were placed together in some kind of tank, in order to encourage them to fight (not that they needed much encouragement). Also, the fact that they were filmed close-up tells us that the fight was planned and observed. Morbid curiosity about camel spider fights is still high. Perhaps this is because it is guaranteed to result in one spider dying, or because their way of fighting (simply stabbing and biting) is so gruesome and gory to watch.

The Complete Guide to Camel Spiders

Camel spiders vs. scorpions

People also seem very curious about camel spiders fighting scorpions. This curiosity began during World War II, when troops stationed in Libya often pitted the two against each other, and continues today.

It is not uncommon for people to search Google or YouTube for 'camel spider vs. scorpion' or 'camel spider fights scorpion.' Possibly, this curiosity is down to the fact that scorpions are considered pretty deadly, with many being venomous, carrying the sting in their tails. Camel spiders are quite similar to scorpions; both have some serious pincers and a fearsome reputation. However, camel spiders are not venomous. So, perhaps when people Google 'camel spider vs. scorpion' or something similar, they are wondering whether camel spiders are so deadly that they can overcome even venomous creatures like scorpions.

One video, entitled 'spider vs. scorpion' shows a camel spider fighting a relatively small scorpion (http://www.youtube.com/watch?v=3Aia2PGJL7s). At the beginning of the video, the camel spider is on its back, but manages to flip over and starts determinedly biting the stinging part of the tail off the scorpion. We do not get to see the end of the fight, but it is safe to assume that the camel spider finished off that scorpion without too much difficulty.

This technique of cutting off the stinging tail seems to be quite common; a few videos depict this outcome. For example, another video shows the camel spider biting the tail of a scorpion nearly clean off, before stabbing at its stomach and killing it (http://www.youtube.com/watch?v=BaNQb7 XzyqQ). This fight only lasts for a matter of minutes; the camel spider easily overcomes this scorpion. It is worth noting that the people talking in the background of this video are speaking Hebrew. Although we cannot be totally sure of the country this is shot in, we can say that interest in camel spiders fighting scorpions is international, and not just present among Western troops.

There is another camel spider vs. scorpion video in which one camel spider is placed in a tank with a number of scorpions (http://www.youtube.com/watch?v=j1A-487F Vg). It is hard to tell how many scorpions there are, about 10. At least four engage in serious battle with the camel spider. Of course, in this case the scorpions win, although it hardly seems fair.

The Complete Guide to Camel Spiders

This is not an exhaustive list of camel spider vs. scorpion videos; there are probably hundreds on YouTube. All the videos mentioned here have quite high viewing numbers. This shows that a strange obsession has developed around these two creatures fighting. This probably both stems from and contributes to the mythic status that camel spiders have achieved.

So, who wins – camel spiders or scorpions? In the wild, they do not regularly fight. However, when they are placed together in a small tank, it is likely that a battle will commence. If it is a fair, one-on-one fight, it will depend on the size and strength of each creature. It also might depend on how hungry each individual is, and when it last fed. This is because, in the wild, animals are likely to fight much harder if they are in need of a meal.

Camel spiders vs. spiders

Camel spiders do often target spiders as prey in the wild, and people sometimes encourage camel spiders to fight with true spiders in captivity.

One video depicts a camel spider killing a black widow in just a few seconds, before going on to slowly consume the corpse (http://www.youtube.com/watch?v =wOGzZW4i4oU). This is quite impressive because black widow spiders have a venomous bite that can be deadly to children or the elderly.

Black Widow

Another video shows a camel spider defeat and consume a wolf spider (http://www.youtube.com/watch?v= Qcd2 RcsZPHo). Wolf spiders are also thought of as ferocious predators and do carry venom, although it has little effect on most humans. Again, the battle is over in minutes.

However, camel spiders are not invincible; there are a number of videos on YouTube that show camel spiders being consumed by tarantulas. Who wins depends on the size and strength of each creature. All we can say is that camel spiders are extremely challenging opponents.

Camel spiders vs. centipedes

Finally, there are even a number of videos in which camel spiders fight giant centipedes. Giant centipedes eat similar prey to camel spiders and also have a painful bite that is not poisonous to humans. These creatures are fairly evenly matched, and the outcome of such battles seems to depend firstly on the size of each individual fighter and

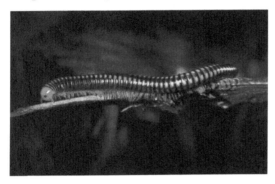 secondly on the arena the fight takes place in.

For example, in one video, a camel spider easily defeats a giant centipede (http://www.youtube.com/watch?v=rWr42nn-yNA). But the centipede either is not fully grown or it is a member of a smaller species. In addition to this, the pair is fighting in a plastic box that is slippery and quite hard for them to grip. Both the size of the centipede and the slippery plastic container are likely to have affected the outcome of the fight.

In another video, the giant centipede is large, and the box is lined with sand and rocks (http://www.youtube.com/watch?v= V2NpalEHF20). The fight takes several minutes, but eventually the centipede comes out on top and the camel spider is killed. This video was shot by American troops stationed in Afghanistan.

People seem to be endlessly interested in fights between camel spiders and other creatures; many videos have been made and have received thousands of views. Whilst it is entertaining to watch, it is not necessarily the most animal-friendly activity, particularly because such creatures rarely fight in the wild. Some believe that staging battles between these creatures is cruel. However, such fights still certainly remain popular among viewers.

The Complete Guide to Camel Spiders

The largest known camel spider

Many people Google phrases such as "huge camel spider," "big camel spider," and "biggest camel spider in the world," as if they will discover some giant camel spider that towers over other creatures. However, in actual fact, camel spiders are not that big.

In the Conservation Institute's list of top ten biggest spiders (or spider-like creatures, given that camel spiders are not really spiders), the camel spider only comes in at number eight. Ahead of the camel spider are several types of tarantula and the huntsman spider, and the goliath bird-eating spider takes the number one spot. It is a myth that camel spiders are the biggest spiders in the world.

Goliath Bird Eating Spider

So what about the largest individual camel spider?

There are many rumours about the biggest camel spider ever seen. Several people claim that they have sighted what they believe to be the largest camel spider in the world. However, many of these claims are either

The Complete Guide to Camel Spiders

fictional or exaggerations. For example, one YouTube video (http://www.youtube.com/watch?v=HosAsCO1FuU) consists only of one picture, shown with music playing in the background. The creature is clearly a camel spider positioned next to a cigarette box. However, even including its legs, the creature does not reach the full length of the box. This is definitely not the world's biggest spider. Although, fair play, this must have been a pretty scary discovery to make in your own house.

We cannot say for sure what size the largest camel spider is, because, of course, not all camel spiders have been seen and measured. However, according to official reports, even the largest camel spiders do not grow beyond six inches in length.

Soldiers' accounts of camel spiders

Western troops serving in places like Iraq and Afghanistan tell interesting, exciting, and often exaggerated stories about camel spiders. Unlike most Westerners, these soldiers might regularly come into close contact with camel spiders and, given that most have never seen such creatures before, they are normally pretty horrified. Possibly, the shock of camel spiders' threatening appearance and their already mythic status, contributes to fear. This can cause further rumours to spread, and a cycle of misinformation to develop.

In this section, we will look at stories and anecdotes from troops. Some of these are true; however, it is important to remember that a few are likely either made-up or wildly exaggerated. We will also describe several videos involving camel spiders that  were filmed by soldiers whilst on duty.

The stories come from a website entitled 'Amazing camel spider Stories.' People, mainly soldiers in some capacity, have sent in stories about their personal

72

The Complete Guide to Camel Spiders

experiences with camel spiders. The videos were found on YouTube.

The Complete Guide to Camel Spiders

Iraq – Anonymous

This story is written by a member of the United States Air Force, stationed in Iraq.

He claims to have seen up to eight camel spiders whilst serving there. However, one camel spider sticks in his mind as particularly nasty.

He recalls seeing the camel spider and chasing (at a distance) behind it. The camel spider crawled inside a crack in a building, and the writer left it for a moment to go and get a friend. However, when the pair returned to get a closer look at the creature, it had disappeared.

Later the same day, a colleague was sat in a truck with his feet hanging outside. Suddenly, the writer heard his colleague screaming and saw him doing a bizarre dance around the truck. Then he noticed a large camel spider fall from the man's shirt; it looked quite similar to the one he had chased earlier. The colleague stamped on the camel spider, and the creature appeared to be dead; its guts were apparently no longer inside its body. The group toyed with the body for some time, before losing interest and leaving it on the tailgate of the truck for over an hour, in direct sunlight, at 120 degrees Fahrenheit.

The writer of this story went back to the body of the camel spider later. He put his knife in between the pincers to see if he could prise them apart. However, to his alarm, the camel spider bit down on his knife. The writer claims that he could pick up the squashed body of the camel spider, just by lifting his knife that was clamped in the camel spider's pincers.

He reports being shocked, because he truly believed that they had killed the creature. The soldier acknowledges that it could have been a nervous reaction; perhaps the camel spider truly was dead. However, he says that this run-in has confirmed in his mind several rumours about the nastiness, viciousness, and strength of camel spiders. They will even bite after they are dead!

Iraq – Louis's story

Louis, also serving in the United States Air Force, saw a camel spider at Baghdad International Airport. Louis claims that this camel spider was about six inches in length. The sun was hot, and he had time to kill, so, out of boredom, Louis started to throw rocks at the camel spider.

He reports that the camel spider turned towards him and slowly started advancing in his direction. Louis continued to throw rocks at the creature to see what it would do next.

Louis states that he finally managed to anger the camel spider, and it bolted towards him "like a car" (ACSS 2013). Needless to say, Louis ran for it. The camel spider then slowed down again, but still advanced towards Louis. He threw a cardboard box in its path, but the camel spider simply walked around it. After some time, the camel spider gave up and moved away.

Louis remains amazed by the aggressive nature of camel spiders. He even jokes that they might be trained by insurgents and sent to attack US troops.

Kuwait – Dave's story

Dave, United States Army, reports walking back from the shower block after dark. He was feeling good, because it was his first hot shower in a week. However, this relaxed mood was soon to be shattered.

Using a flashlight, Dave suddenly noticed movement in the sand next to him as he walked. He directed the torch straight at the spot, and, to his terror, saw a camel spider charging at him. Dave claims that this camel spider was "bigger than a kitten" (ACSS 2013). He also states that it left a dust trail of sand hanging in the air behind it as it ran. Dave ran as fast as he could back to his tent and made it unscathed.

This was not Dave's only sighting of a camel spider and he says that he eventually began to accept them as part of the daily routine while on duty. However, he also claims that if he ever sees one again he may have some kind of nervous breakdown. Back in the United States, Dave says that the arachnophobia he experienced before his time in the Army has now completely gone. This is because no spiders where he lives compare to the terrifying camel spiders he saw whilst on duty.

Dave still has nightmares about camel spiders and believes that these creatures alone are enough to give someone post-traumatic stress disorder.

Video – The prank

In this video, two US soldiers search frantically for a camel spider that is running loose in their dorm (http://www.youtube.com/watch?v =dQRKjoAr_q8). This appears to be a cruel prank courtesy of their comrades.

Voices in the background can be heard discussing how the camel spider was found outside before being caught, wrapped in a t-shirt, and thrown into the soldiers' dorm. The two soldiers who are the butt of the joke had been trying to get some sleep; both are dressed only in boxer shorts. One soldier is stood on his bed and clutching a gun. The other is carrying what appears to be part of some exercise equipment or a broken fold-up chair, and he is searching frantically for the creature.

Both are very angry, and one of the soldiers shouts, "I'm so scared of these things" (YouTube 2011d). The soldiers are clearly not going to be able to continue sleeping with the camel spider still in the room.

The hunt carries on for about five minutes. The camel spider is sighted twice, but it manages to run away and hide under the bed. The third time the soldiers see the camel spider, one manages to pound it with his weapon of choice. The camel spider is squashed and killed.

This video tells us about the reputation that camel spiders have within the US Army. The fact that such a prank was played shows that the soldiers were aware of how much fear a camel spider could create. Although the two pranked soldiers were laughing and playing along with the joke, it is clear that both were quite distressed and would not attempt to go back to sleep until the camel spider was dead.

It is important to note that at no point did the camel spider try to attack. Instead, it was attempting to hide and run away. Therefore, this calls into question the rumours about camel spiders having no fear of humans and attacking everything they come into contact with.

Video – Camel spider in a cup

This video is pretty amusing. Some soldiers have managed to capture a camel spider (http://www.youtube.com/watch ?v=TJkLb-UIGHM). The creature is being held captive in a cup, with a clear plastic bag stretched over the top so it cannot escape.

The soldier holding this cup waves it in the face of another soldier, who appears to be standing on a chair or table. This soldier clearly does not see the plastic bag protection, and he panics. He jumps backwards against a wall and falls off the chair/table. He is left sitting on the floor looking fairly embarrassed. The rest of the soldiers laugh and gloat as expected, as the soldier with bruised pride walks out.

Again, this video shows that even stereotypically tough soldiers do fear camel spiders.

The Complete Guide to Camel Spiders

Afghanistan – Nicole's story

Nicole's story is quite different to the others; she does not find camel spiders terrifying or vicious at all.

Whilst serving in Afghanistan, Nicole claims to have kept a camel spider as a pet for about six months and describes the creature as "beautiful and sweet" (ACSS 2013).

Nicole seems to be aware of the facts about camel spiders; she explains that they are not poisonous and that bites simply lead to infections. Nicole says that she was never bitten and that she managed to handle her camel spider for hours on end. Alongside Nicole's story, there are indeed pictures of a camel spider. In these pictures, Nicole is holding the camel spider and allowing it to crawl all over her, even on her head (she was wearing a hat).

Nicole does report that the camel spider fought fiercely with anything that was placed alongside it in the enclosure. However, she maintains that her camel spider was "the sweetest thing" (ACSS 2013).

When Nicole had to let her camel spider go, it followed her for some time, until she found it a nice shady spot. She says that she never saw the camel spider run or jump in the entire six months she cared for it.

Nicole states that most stories about camel spiders are urban legends based on surprise encounters for both parties. She says that, even though a lot of people thought she was crazy, she loved her camel spider and wishes she could have brought it home with her from Afghanistan.

Nicole's story shows that all the hype about camel spiders probably is unnecessary. As she says, both people and camel spiders are likely to be shocked and alarmed by the presence of the other. This causes extreme reactions and defensive behaviour from both parties – for example, hissing and threatening behaviour from camel spiders, or running away, throwing rocks, and trying to stamp on the creature from humans. In reality, the best response if you see a camel spider is to calmly move away.

The case of a camel spider in the UK

The hype about camel spiders intensified when paratrooper Rodney Griffiths accidentally brought one home with him from Afghanistan.

Griffiths had been serving in Helmand Province for four months before his visit home in June 2008. He was happy to escape the dangers and discomfort of living in the desert. However, he had inadvertently packed an unwelcome passenger – a camel spider.

Still unaware of the unpleasant gift he had brought back for his family, Griffiths returned to duty several weeks later. It wasn't until seven weeks after Griffiths initially returned from Afghanistan that the camel spider was eventually discovered in the family home. The thought of the creature roaming around the house after dark, without the occupants having any knowledge of it, is quite creepy.

The camel spider was initially discovered by the couple's son Ricky (16), who was searching for underwear in a drawer before feeling something large and hairy crawl over his hand. Ricky shouted his sister, Cassie (18), and the pair tried to catch the camel spider by putting a pint glass over it. However, the camel spider's long legs would not fit inside the glass. They tried to poke the camel spider with a coat hanger and were highly alarmed when the creature attempted to bite said coat hanger. At this point, the family dog, Bella, entered the room and immediately started barking at the camel spider. In response, the camel spider let out a loud hissing sound, and Bella ran out of the room pretty quickly. An electrician who was working in the house at the time went to take a look at the camel spider, but also ran in terror when he laid eyes on it.

The family initially did not know what the threatening looking creature invading their home was. However, an extensive Google search revealed that it was a camel spider, and understanding began to dawn when they discovered that camel spiders often inhabit places like Afghanistan.

The family left out various traps to try and catch the camel spider, but to no avail. Any meat left out was always consumed, but they still could not manage to catch the creature. Believing that the camel spider had nested in Cassie's room, the family decided to move out until the intruder was caught.

Several different people attempted to catch the camel spider, including an Army Welfare Officer and the Royal

Society for the Prevention of Cruelty to Animals (RSPCA). The RSPCA caught a spider, believing it might be the culprit, only to be told that the spider they had caught was very different to what the Griffiths family had seen. All searches were unsuccessful, and Mrs Griffiths said the family would not return home until the camel spider was captured and removed.

The key part of the story, which has caused many rumours to spread about camel spiders, is that the family dog, Bella, died shortly after her brief run-in with the camel spider. The family noticed that Bella had a high temperature and a swollen stomach, so they took her to the local vet surgery. Sadly, tests revealed that Bella had a low white cell count, and the decision was taken to put her down. Mrs Griffiths has claimed that Bella was a healthy and active dog of only eight years, and thinks it is an unlikely coincidence that she died during the same period that the camel spider was discovered in the house. Mrs Griffiths wonders if the spider bit Bella or "sprayed something into her face when it hissed at her" (Daily Mail 2008). The vet said that without an autopsy they could not say for certain what caused Bella's sudden illness, but it is possible that the stress of the situation brought on a previously-unrecognised, underlying condition.

This story has led to some seriously bad press for camel spiders, who are now viewed as dangerous, pet-killing invaders that are cunning and experts at escaping capture. We can say with a high degree of certainty that the camel spider did not spray anything into Bella's face. As we have previously discussed, the hissing sound that camel spiders create is called stridulating. This rubbing together of the pincers is not harmful, but merely meant to ward off predators when the camel spider is feeling threatened. It is possible that the camel spider bit the dog when the family were not watching, and this could have led to an infection possibly resulting in death. Or, as the vet said, it is possible that the incident caused Bella significant stress that exacerbated an underlying condition.

The RSPCA stated that camel spiders do not normally attack humans, but they can give a painful bite if you are unlucky. This is correct, and some might believe that moving out of their family home is an unnecessary measure for the Griffiths. After all, these creatures often creep inside homes in Afghanistan and other places. However, even in possession of all the facts about camel spiders – such as that they are not poisonous and they do not normally attack humans – it is fairly understandable that the Griffiths family has chosen not to live with the camel spider. The thought of one of these creatures lurking in the shadows is quite unpleasant and, as the RSPCA stated, they can give a nasty bite. Ricky was lucky not to be bitten when he first reached into the drawer and felt the camel spider. It is also worth mentioning that the Griffiths have a four-year-old daughter, Ellie-Rose. A young child might not understand the concept of 'don't touch the scary looking spider,' and this could have nasty consequences. Therefore, the Griffiths decision to move out temporarily is not totally unreasonable, although this story has generally given out an unnecessarily negative perception of camel spiders.

Myths about camel spiders

There are many myths about camel spiders circulating, and all are either wild exaggerations or completely untrue.

These rumours stem from both local people living in places that camel spiders inhabit, and Western troops stationed in war zones that are home to camel spiders. Several pictures and stories on the Internet have contributed to a kind of mass phobia of camel spiders, and the film entitled 'Camel Spiders' has encouraged their terrifying reputation (http://www.youtube.com/watch?v=X-VM9X-uRmE). In reality, camel spiders are generally not harmful to us and do not pose a serious threat to humanity.

In this section we will look at some of the most common myths that are currently circulating about camel spiders. We will investigate whether there is any truth to these myths, and if not, why they have come to be widely considered as fact.

Man-eaters

The first rumour that many people take as fact is that camel spiders hunt humans and eat their flesh.

This is simply not true. Camel spiders will not go after humans, but instead try to avoid them. Like other creatures, camel spiders are afraid of humans because we are so much bigger than them.

Camel spiders can give a painful bite, but only if they are startled or antagonised.

Instead, camel spiders' choice of food tends to include insects like crickets, spiders, small lizards, termites, and occasionally small snakes and birds.

As we can see, humans do not feature in the diet of a camel spider.

Numbing poison

The second widely-believed myth about camel spiders is that they have venom that is released when they bite. People think that this venom numbs the flesh in the area surrounding the initial bite. It is said that this allows the camel spider to then gnaw and consume large chunks of flesh. People have claimed that they have been attacked in their sleep and woken up with huge portions of flesh missing from their limbs – supposedly the work of a camel spider.

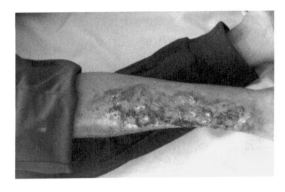

Again, we can say that this is largely complete nonsense. Camel spiders do occasionally bite people in their sleep. This is a possibility because these creatures sometimes try to find shade from the sun in tents or houses. However, a bite normally only occurs if the person inadvertently rolls on top of the camel spider or touches and alarms it in some way.

Camel spiders do not possess any poison or venom; they simply bite and stab their prey to death. They do use digestive juices to liquefy their meal so it is easy to consume, but this is in no way poisonous or numbing.

90

The bite from a camel spider is likely to be quite painful. They have the largest jaws compared to their size in the world. This is normally sufficiently noticeable to wake someone up. There is no need to worry about finding large areas of flesh missing; if a camel spider bites you, it is sure to be in self-defence, and the creature will make a speedy getaway before any flesh is consumed.

This myth possibly stems from people who have developed serious infections from camel spider bites. This is a risk, and if you do receive a bite from a camel spider, the area should be properly cleaned and bandaged.

Laying eggs in wounds

This myth is very gruesome and completely false. Several people have claimed that camel spiders lay their eggs in the open wounds of large creatures, humans included! This can be directly after a camel spider bite, or the wound could have been obtained in a different manner. The wound is then said to heal up, with the victim unaware of what has taken place. The end result is thousands of baby camel spiders puncturing the skin and crawling out of the victim's body.

The thought of this is very repulsive. However, we can rest easy, because this does not happen. Instead, camel spiders dig burrows or find some other sheltered place, for example under a rock, to lay their eggs.

Half the size of a human

If you ask someone at random how big they think a camel spider is, they might say the size of a Frisbee, a dinner plate, a hubcap, one foot in length, or even half the size of a human.

Generally, the size of camel spiders is wildly exaggerated. This is often exacerbated by pictures of camel spiders on the Internet. For example, one picture, which has been viewed by many people, is of a soldier stationed in a desert environment holding up two camel spiders. The shot makes it looks like the camel spiders in question reach the soldiers waist (length-wise). However, the camel spiders are positioned much closer to the lens than the soldier. The result of this perspective is that the camel spiders appear much larger than they actually are.

In reality, camel spiders do not grow that big. Many species of camel spider are considered to be fairly small Arachnids and the largest species can still only grow to about six inches in length.

It is possible that rumours about size have developed because people are so shocked by the (undeniably terrifying) appearance of camel spiders on first sight, it causes them to remember the creature as much larger than it actually was. It is also possible that people exaggerate their run-ins with camel spiders in order to impress or captivate others. It is safe to say that camel spiders have never been known to grow to half the size of a human.

Chasing people

Another common myth about camel spiders is that they chase humans. This is often thought to be with the intention of attacking.

Again, this is not true. As we have already mentioned, camel spiders are likely to be threatened by humans and will try to avoid us the majority of the time.

However, there is one exception to this rule, which explains why this myth has developed. Sometimes camel spiders do run after humans, but this is not because they want to bite or attack the person. Instead, they are chasing the shade that the human was providing. This is typical in desert environments where there is little shelter from the sun. The shadow of a person, sitting or standing, can provide some respite from the hot sun for the camel spider. If the person moves, the camel spider might follow, appearing as if it chasing after the person, but really it is just trying to stay in the shade.

The Complete Guide to Camel Spiders

Eating the stomachs of camels

Some people think that camel spiders got their name because they eat camels – specifically, because they leap from the desert floor and grip onto the stomach of the camel, before biting through the skin and eating the stomach.

This myth is untrue; camel spiders do not consume any type of large mammals (including camels and humans). Instead, as we have previously covered, they mostly eat insects, spiders, and lizards.

Camel spiders do not eat camels. However, they do share the same name. This is possibly because they have similar attributes to camels such as they often live in desert-like conditions, some species are a sandy colour, and they can go for a long time without drinking water.

The scream

Camel spiders' scream has become a widely-discussed feature. Camel spiders are believed to let off a banshee-type wail as they run towards their prey in the lead up to an attack. The scream is generally considered to be a terrifying signal that the camel spider is going to bite or attack.

However, we know that camel spiders do not 'scream' as such. Some species stridulate. This is not normally a sign of attack, but rather a method of attracting a mate. In other cases, stridulating can be a warning that the camel spider is feeling threatened. In this situation, if you just move away, the camel spider will not attack. It can be assumed that the 'scream' is actually just this stridulating behaviour, which is not something to be worried about. Although understandably the sound can be alarming if the person is unaware of what it means, this is probably how the myth developed.

Vastly exaggerated speed

People often exaggerate the speed at which camel spiders can move. It has been said that camel spiders can run at 30 miles per hour or they can outrun humans.

Again, this is simply untrue. Camel spiders have a top speed of about 10 miles per hour. For their size, this is quite impressive; however, they could not match the speed of a human being.

People also claim that spiders can leap high into the air – three feet high is the figure that has been spread around. However, this is impossible; camel spiders are not known to do any significant jumping.

Conclusions about camel spiders

In this book, we have looked at the facts and confronted some of the popular myths and rumours about camel spiders.

People are very curious about camel spiders, particularly their aggressive appearance; phrases like 'camel spider pictures,' 'pics of camel spiders,' 'camel spider images,' and 'camel spider bite pictures' are often typed into Google. Sadly, this is not because we like and want to know more about camel spiders. Instead, as we have recognised throughout this book, it is because many people believe that camel spiders are ferocious, vicious, and all-round evil beings. However, this is not the case. Camel spiders are wild creatures that are unfortunately not blessed with particularly good looks. People do not have the same prejudices about lions and tigers, which are generally considered beautiful, even though they are highly aggressive predators.

Camel spiders are not evil; they are simply trying to survive in what can often be a harsh environment. They will defend themselves if they feel threatened, as other wild animals would, and they are undeniably tough predators. But they do not hunt humans – this is a myth!

It is our hope that this book has gone some way to rectifying the terrible reputation that camel spiders have developed. Camel spiders are very interesting and are highly adapted and evolved to life in the wild. We should recognise them as the fascinating creatures that they are.

A Note Regarding Photos and Video Links.

All photos used in this text were legally purchased from stock photo suppliers and inserted according to the purchase rules. Stock photographers grant purchasers the right to use photos without attribution. No images in this text were copied from any illegal source or used without the permission of the photographer. The video links were accurate at the time of publishing.

The Complete Guide to Camel Spiders

Bibliography

Amazing Camel Spider Stories (ACSS) (2013) Amazing 'real' camel spider stories from all over the world!, Accessed 25/10/2013, http://www.camelspiders.net/camel-spider.htm

Archibald, B. (2012) Daily Mail, *Under Attack... From a Spider: How One Soldier Spent Three Months in Hospital after Being Bitten during a Tour of Iraq*, Accessed 11/10/2013, http://www.dailymail.co.uk/news/article-2116970/Soldier-Sammy-O-Gorman-hospitalised-bitten-spider-Iraq.html

Armstrong, A. M. (2013) Paw Nation, *Care of a Camel Spider*, Accessed 19/10/2013, http://animals.pawnation.com/care-camel-spider-4205.html

BBC (2013a) Nature, Wildlife, *Camel Spiders*, Accessed 01/10/2013, http://www.bbc.co.uk/nature/life/Solifugae

BBC (2013b) Nature, Wildlife, *Scorpions*, Accessed 01/10/2013, http://www.bbc.co.uk/nature/life/Scorpion

BBC (2013c) Nature, Wildlife, *Spiders*, Accessed 01/10/2013, http://www.bbc.co.uk/nature/life/Spider

BBC (2013d) Nature, Wildlife, *Dry Tolerant*, Accessed 03/10/2013, http://www.bbc.co.uk/nature/adaptations/Desiccation_tolerance

BBC (2013e) Nature, Wildlife, *Desert*, Accessed 09/10/2013, http://www.bbc.co.uk/nature/habitats/Deserts_and_xeric_s hrublands

BioKids (2013) Critter Catalogue, *Wolf spiders: Lycosidae*, Accessed 21/10/2013, http://www.biokids.umich .edu/critters/Lycosidae/

Cancello, E. M. and Rocha, L. S. (2002) Re-description of *Metacleobis Fulvipes* Roewer from Brazil (Solifugae, Mummuciidae), *Journal of Arachnology*, Vol. 30, No. 1, 104-109.

Carlsen, N. R. (2013) *8 Spider Myths You Probably Believe*, Accessed 23/10/2013, http://www.therollerskate.com /articles/ stuff-i-wanna-write-about/8-spider-myths

Conservation Institute (2013) 10 of the World's Largest Spiders, Accessed 25/10/2013, http://www.conservationin stitute.org/10-of-the-worlds-largest-spiders/

Daily Mail (2008) Spider 'kills' pet dog after paratrooper brings it home from Afghanistan, Accessed 23/10/2013, http://www.dailymail.co.uk/news/article-1049755/Spider-kills-pet-dog-paratrooper-accidentally-brings-home-Afghanistan.html

Dunlop, J. A. (2005) The Arachnid Order Solifugae, *Introduction: Fossil History*, Accessed 03/10/2013, http://www.solpugid.com/Fossil%20History.htm

Exotic Pets (2013) Exotic Pets: Home of the Alternative Pet, *Camel Spider*, Accessed 19/10/2013, http://www.exotic-pets.co.uk/camel-spider.html

Furman, J. (2005) The Arachnid Order Solifugae, *Solifuges as Scavengers*, Accessed, 11/10/2013, http://www.solpugidc om /Scavenging%20%20Behavior.htm

Gaille, S. (2013) *The Camel Spider*, South Carolina: CreateSpace Independent Publishing Platform.

Gromov, A., Hrušková-Martišová, M., and Pekár, S. (2007) Biology of *Galeodes Caspius Subfuscus* (Solifugae, Galeodidae), *Journal of Arachnology*, Vol. 35, No. 3, pp. 546-550.

Grylls, B. (2006) *Man vs. Wild*, Accessed 15/10/2013, http://www.youtube.com/watch?v=cJRpXYs1pQA

Grylls, B. (2009) *Mission Survival 3: Sands of the Scorpion*, Salisbury: Red Fox Publishers.

Haggerty, K. (2012) MMA Mania, *UFC's Stephan Bonnar Bitten by Giant Camel Spider While Detained by Bahrain Airport Security*, Accessed 11/10/2013, http://www.mmamania.com /2012/4/24/2970434/ufcsstephan-bonnar-bitten-by-giant-camel-spider-while-being-detained

Harvey, M. S. (2002) The Neglected Cousins: What do we Know about the Smaller Arachnid Orders?, *The Journal of Arachnology*, Vol. 30, pp. 357–372.

Kirkham, D. (2013) Frontline Pests, *5 Myths about the Camel Spider (Solifugae)*, Accessed 23/10/2013, http://www.frontlinepest.com/blog/5-myths-about-the-camel-spider/

Klann, A. E. (2005) The Arachnid Order Solifugae, *Introduction: Physiology*, Accessed 03/10/2013, http://www.solpugid.com/Physiology.htm

Live Science (2013) *Camel Spiders: Facts and Myths*, Accessed 02/10/2013, http://www.livescience.com/40025-camel-spiders-facts.html

National Geographic (2012) Animals, *Black Widow Spider (Latrodectus Hesperus)*, Accessed 21/10/13, http://animals.nationalgeographic.co.uk/animals/bugs/black-widow-spider

National Geographic (2013) Animals, *Egyptian Giant Solpugid (Camel Spider)*, Accessed 05/10/2013, http://animals.nationalgeographic.co.uk/animals/bugs/egyptian-giant-solpugid/

Punzo, F. (1998) *The Biology of Camel-Spiders: Arachnida, Solifugae,* Massachusetts: Kluwer Academic Publishers.

Real Monstrosities (2010) Giant Centipede, Accessed 21/10/2013, http://www.realmonstrosities.com/2010/12/giant-centipede.html

Reddick, K. (2005) The Arachnid Order Solifugae, *Predators,* Accessed 11/10/2013, http://www.solpugid.com/Predators .htm

Reddick, K. and Wharton, R. A. (2005a) The Arachnid Order Solifugae, *Courtship and Mating,* Accessed 05/10/2013, http://www.solpugid.com/Courtship%20and%20Mating.htm

Reddick, K. and Wharton, R. A. (2005b) The Arachnid Order Solifugae, *Life History,* Accessed 05/10/2013, http://www.solpugid.com/Life%20History.htm

Reddick, K. and Wharton, R. A. (2005c) The Arachnid Order Solifugae, *Prey,* Accessed 09/10/2013, http://www.solpugid.com/Prey.htm

Reddick, K. and Wharton, R. A. (2005d) The Arachnid Order Solifugae, *Hunting Behaviour,* Accessed, 11/10/2013, http://www.solpugid.com/Hunting%20Behavior.htm

Savary, W. E. (2005a) The Arachnid Order Solifugae, *Introduction: What are Solifuges?*, Accessed 03/10/2013, http://www.solpugid.com/Introduction.htm

Savary, W. E. (2005b) The Arachnid Order Solifugae, *Mimicry*, Accessed 03/10/2013, http://www.solpugid.com/Mimicry.htm

Savary, W. E. (2005c) The Arachnid Order Solifugae, *Phylogeny/Taxonomy*, Accessed 08/10/2013, http://www.solpugid.com/Ammotrechidae.htm

Savary, W. E. (2005d) The Arachnid Order Solifugae, *Biology, Behaviour and Ecology*, Accessed 09/10/2013, http://www.solpugid.com/Biology-Ecology.htm

Schogol, J (2011) Stars and Stripes, *Should You be Afraid of Camel Spider?*, Accessed 15/10/2013, http://www.stripes.com /blogs/the-rumor-doctor/the-rumor-doctor-1.104348/should-you-be-afraid-of-camel-spiders-1.136674

Shapiro, L. (2012) Encyclopaedia of Life, *Solifugae (sun spiders): Brief Summary*, Accessed 02/10/2013, http://eol.org/pages/8547/details#distribution

Speed of Animals (2013) *Domestic Cat*, Accessed 02/10/2013, http://www.speedofanimals.com/animals/domestic_cat

Spider Bite Treatment (2013) *Camel Spiders*, Accessed 11/10/2013, http://www.spiderbitetreatment.com/camel-spiders/

Spiders World (2009) Spider Facts and Information. *Camel Spider*, Accessed 05/10/2013, http://www.spidersworlds.com/camel-spider.html

Vigil, S. (2013) Paw Nation, *Camel Spider Facts and Myths*, Accessed 23/10/2013, http://animals.pawnation.com/camel-spider-myths-4297.html

YouTube (2007) camel spider fight, Accessed 21/10/2013, http://www.youtube.com/watch?v=RMP3F1VsCkg

YouTube (2009a) scorpions vs camel spider, Accessed 21/10/2013, http://www.youtube.com/watch?v=j1A-487F_Vg

YouTube (2009b) World's Biggest Spider (By Far) Found in a local resident's house!, Accessed 25/10/2013, http://www.youtube.com/watch?v=HosAsCO1FuU

YouTube (2010a) spider vs scorpion, Accessed 21/10/2013, http://www.youtube.com/watch?v=3Aia2PGJL7s

YouTube (2010b) camel spider vs scorpion and an Ant, Accessed 21/10/2013, http://www.youtube.com /watch?v=BaNQb7XzyqQ

YouTube (2011a) Hades my SUPER FRIENDLY CAMEL SPIDER, Accessed 19/10/2013, http://www.youtube.com /watch?v=BejAWXq15mA

YouTube (2011b) Black Widow Vs. Camel Spider, Accessed 21/10/2013, http://www.youtube.com/watch?v =wOGzZW4i4oU

YouTube (2011c) Camel Spider VS Centipede, Accessed 21/10/2013, http://www.youtube.com/watch?v=rWr42nn-yNA

YouTube (2011d) Soldiers VS Camel Spider, Accessed 25/10/2013, http://www.youtube.com/watch?v =dQRKjoAr_q8

YouTube (2012a) Camel spider feeding – Adult locust!, Accessed 19/10/2013, http://www.youtube.com /watch?v=Kq_JMgDDIiw

YouTube (2012b) Angry Camel Spider!, Accessed 19/10/2013, http://www.youtube.com/watch?v =ommiDuKb8iE

YouTube (2012c) Camel Spider vs. Wolf Spider, Accessed 21/10/2013, http://www.youtube.com/watch?v= Qcd2RcsZPHo

YouTube (2012d) Camel Spiders (2012) – Official Trailer, Accessed 23/10/2013, http://www.youtube.com/watch?v=X-VM9X-uRmE

YouTube (2012e) Soldier vs Camel Spider, Accessed 25/10/2013, http://www.youtube.com/watch?v=TJkLb-UIGHM

YouTube (2013) Leroy the Camel Spider vs. Centipede, FOB Tombstone Afghanistan, Accessed 21/10/2013, http://www.youtube.com/watch?v=V2NpalEHF20

Index

CPSIA information can be obtained at www.ICGtesting.com
Printed in the USA
LVOW01s1616100314

376785LV00014B/73/P

9 780992 676728